The Voyages of Odysseus

Author:
Sue Reid began writing stories when she was a child and now writes for BBC Schools Radio. Her first book – *Mill Girl* – was published by Scholastic in 2002. She would like to dedicate *The Voyages of Odysseus* to William, Matt and Guy.

Artist:
Mark Bergin studied at Eastbourne College of Art and has illustrated many children's books. He lives in Bexhill-on-Sea with his wife and three children.

Series creator:
David Salariya was born in Dundee, Scotland. He has illustrated a wide range of books and has created and designed many new series for publishers both in the UK and overseas. In 1989, he established The Salariya Book Company. He lives in Brighton with his wife, illustrator Shirley Willis, and their son Jonathan.

Editor:
Michael Ford

Published in Great Britain in 2004 by
Book House, an imprint of
The Salariya Book Company Ltd
25 Marlborough Place, Brighton BN1 1UB

Please visit the Salariya Book Company at:
www.salariya.com
www.book-house.co.uk

ISBN 1 904642 31 4

A catalogue record
for this book is available from the British Library.

Printed and bound in China.

Printed on paper
from sustainable forests.

Ancient Greek Myths

The Voyages of Odysseus

Written by
Sue Reid

Illustrated by
Mark Bergin

Created and designed by
David Salariya

BOOK HOUSE

The world of Ancient Greek mythology

The Ancient Greek civilisation was one of the greatest in the history of the world. It spanned nearly two thousand years, until it was eventually overtaken by the Roman Empire in the second century BC. At its height, the Greek world extended far beyond what we know as modern Greece.

We owe much to the Ancient Greeks. They were great scientists, mathematicians, dramatists and philosophers. They were also brilliant storytellers. Many of the tales they told were in the form of poetry, often thousands of lines long. The Greeks wrote poems about all kinds of human experience – love, friendship, war, revenge, history and even simple everyday activities. The most famous of the poems which have passed down to us are the epic tales of courage and warfare, where brave heroes struggle and suffer against great odds.

A map showing the Ancient Greek mainland, surrounding islands and neighbouring lands

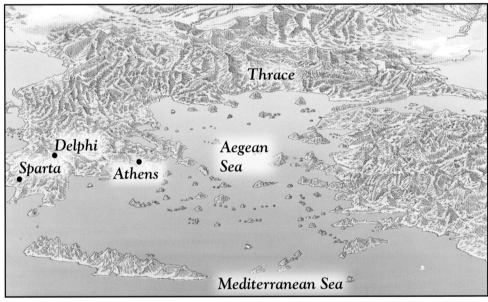

Thrace

Delphi

Sparta

Athens

Aegean Sea

Mediterranean Sea

It is incredible that until the eighth century BC, the Greeks had no established form of writing. All of their stories, lengthy as they were, were handed down through every generation by word of mouth. The people who passed on these tales were professional storytellers. They would perform in town squares or public theatres. Often several versions of the same myth existed, depending on who told it and when it was told. What follows is one version of the voyages of Odysseus.

If you need help with any of the names, go to the pronunciation guide on page 31.

introduction

Gather round and hear my story. I shall tell you about one of the greatest heroes Greece has ever known – the brave Odysseus, king of the island Ithaca. His story began when he joined his Greek comrades to fight the city of Troy. For ten years they besieged the city until Odysseus – the most cunning of the Greeks – found a way to trick the Trojans and end the war. He and some warriors hid inside a huge wooden horse, hoping that the Trojans would drag it into the city. Foolishly, this is just what they did! At night the Greeks climbed out and opened the city gates for their comrades. Surprised by their enemies, the Trojans were defeated. Sick of war and eager to be reunited with his wife, Penelope, Odysseus and his fleet of twelve ships were at last able to go home.

5

From one feast to the next

Travelling back to Ithaca, Odysseus and his men first put ashore at Ismarus, a city in Thrace. They rampaged through the city, looting and killing, before hurrying back to their boats. Odysseus wisely wanted to leave before the locals could seek revenge, but his men chose to feast and then fell into a drunken sleep. They were woken by the shouts of the Cicones, neighbouring warriors who had come to avenge the deaths of their friends. There was bloody fighting, and though the Greeks escaped to their ships, 72 men were killed.

Grieving for their dead comrades, the men sailed onward to the land of the Lotus-Eaters. There Odysseus sent three of his men to spy out the land. But they didn't return and he went in search of them. At last Odysseus found the men lolling about in a daze and dragged them back to their ships.

The raid on Ismarus

The Greeks plundered the city of Ismarus, helping themselves to treasure and supplies of water, food and wine for their voyage home.

Ask the storyteller

What made Odysseus's men so dozy?

The Lotus-Eaters had given the men the fruit of the lotus plant to eat. It made the men forget all about who they were and their voyage home.

Polyphemus the cyclops

Sailing on, the men reached the land of the cyclops. Odysseus was eager to find out what these one-eyed giants were like and led a party of men into one of their caves. Soon its owner returned – the gigantic Polyphemus – with one eye staring out from the middle of his forehead. Polyphemus was very angry to find the men in his home and straightaway seized and ate two of them for his supper. Then he made sure the others couldn't escape by blocking the cave's entrance with a huge boulder. The men were terrified, but the wily Odysseus soon worked out a way to escape. The following night, while Polyphemus was asleep, they sharpened a wooden stake and blinded the cyclops with it. In the morning, when Polyphemus rolled away the boulder to let his sheep out, the men sneaked out as well. The enraged cyclops called on the god Poseidon for revenge.

Odysseus tricks the cyclops

In the morning the blinded Polyphemus sat in the cave entrance and felt his sheep's woolly backs to make sure that the men didn't slip out too. He didn't find them though, because they were tied under the sheep's bellies.

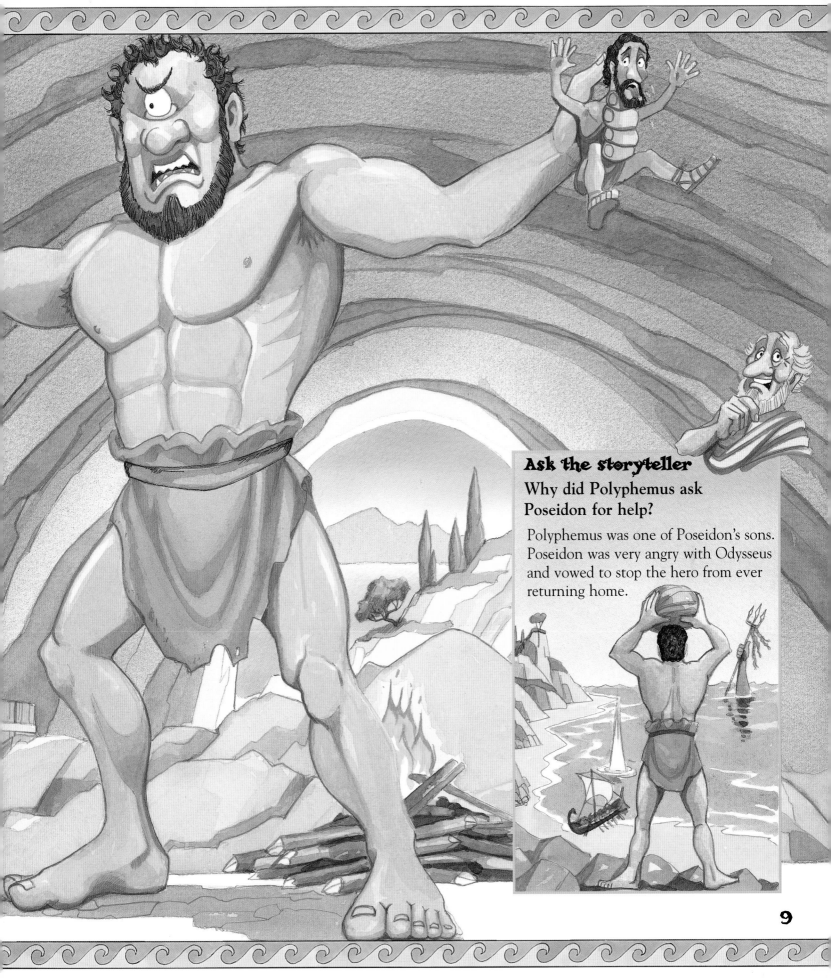

9

Keeper of the Winds

Next Odysseus and his men reached the island ruled by King Aeolus, the god of the winds. Aeolus welcomed Odysseus and gave him a mysterious leather bag, which he told him never to open. Then he sent a gentle breeze after the ships to guide them home. But when Odysseus's back was turned, the greedy crew opened the bag, looking for treasure. Out rushed terrible storms, which drove the ships back to the island. This time Aeolus refused to help them. Worse was to come. Setting out again they were blown to the land of the Laestrygonians. There the unfortunate crew met King Antiphates, a man-eating giant, who promptly gobbled up another of Odysseus's men. The rest of the men fled back to their ships, chased by the giants.

The Laestrygonians

The angry Laestrygonians pursued Odysseus's men as they fled back to their ships, hurling boulders and spears at them as they tried to escape. Trapped in the harbour, all the ships were sunk, except Odysseus's.

Ask the storyteller

How did Odysseus manage to escape?

Odysseus had wisely moored his ship outside the harbour. In this way he was able to cast anchor quickly and so sail out of danger.

Circe the enchantress

Mourning their dead friends, Odysseus and his crew sailed on to Circe's island. Upon landing, some of the men went to Circe's house to seek help. Circe was a wicked sorceress, who used her magic to turn men into beasts. All round her house were tame lions and wolves – men who'd been bewitched by Circe. She made Odysseus's men very welcome, but after they'd eaten and drunk her delicious food, she struck them with her wand and turned them into pigs. Only one man, Eurylochus, escaped, as he'd wisely stayed outside. When he saw what had happened to his comrades he rushed back to the ship to warn Odysseus. Odysseus set off at once to confront Circe. On his way he met Hermes, messenger of the gods, who showed the hero how to protect himself against Circe's magic.

Odysseus confronts Circe

When Circe struck Odysseus with her wand, he quickly drew his sword. Fearful that Odysseus meant to kill her, Circe immediately agreed to turn his men back into humans.

Ask the storyteller

How did Hermes protect Odysseus?

Circe secretly mixed a magic potion into the men's food to make them forget where they came from. Hermes gave Odysseus a plant called Moly to put into any food that Circe might offer. This protected him from her magic.

To the Underworld

Circe told Odysseus to visit the Underworld and ask the dead prophet Tiresias how to find his way home. Odysseus was dismayed, for no one ever returned from the Underworld, the home of dead spirits. But he did as Circe instructed. In the Underworld Tiresias warned Odysseus that he'd made an enemy of Poseidon. He told Odysseus that they might still get home safely, as long as they didn't harm the cattle on the Sun God's island. Many other spirits came up to speak to Odysseus, including his mother and his old comrade, the warrior Achilles. Odysseus also saw Sisyphus, who spent his days trying, in vain, to roll a boulder up a mountain as punishment by the gods for his sins. So many wailing spirits pressed round Odysseus that he hurried back to his ship in fear.

Odysseus's mother

Odysseus saw his mother's spirit in the Underworld. He didn't even know that she had died and, overcome by grief, he tried to embrace her. She warned him that, in his absence, his family faced troubles back at home on Ithaca.

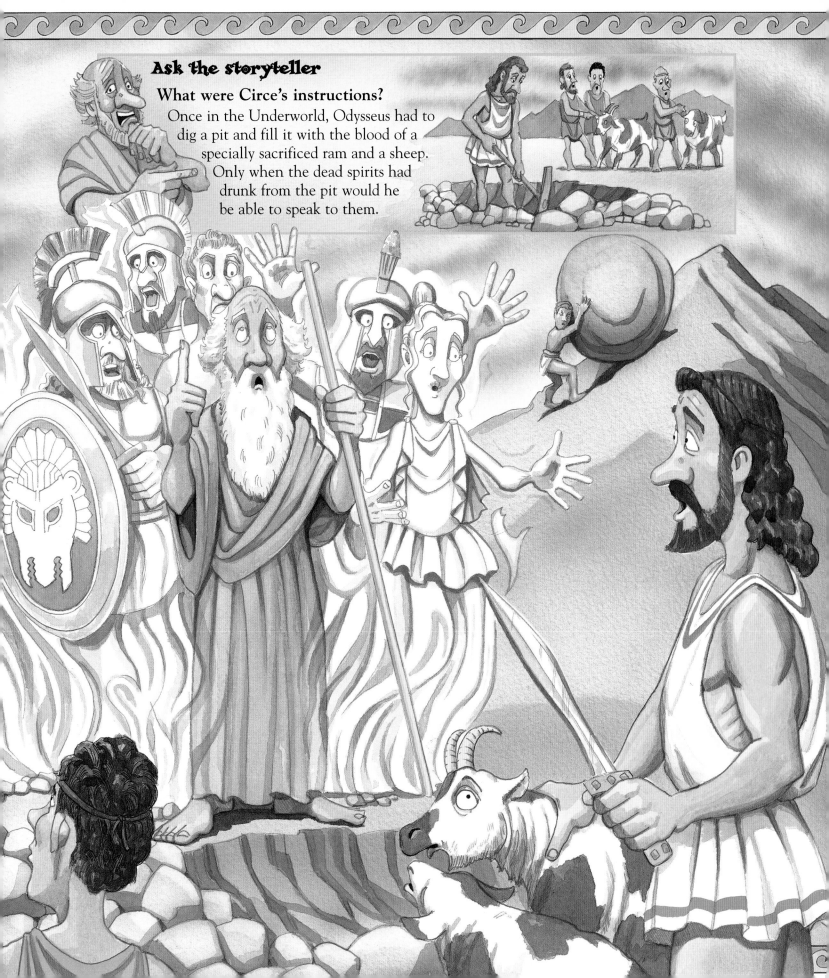

Ask the storyteller

What were Circe's instructions?

Once in the Underworld, Odysseus had to dig a pit and fill it with the blood of a specially sacrificed ram and a sheep. Only when the dead spirits had drunk from the pit would he be able to speak to them.

Beware Sirens!

Circe was overjoyed when Odysseus returned safely from the Underworld. She wanted to help him, so she gave him instructions on how to avoid the perils that lay ahead. The men soon reached the first of these – the island of the Sirens. The Sirens were part woman, part bird. Their enchanted singing lured all who heard it to their doom on the rocks. Following Circe's advice, Odysseus filled his men's ears with wax so that they wouldn't hear the beautiful songs. Then he ordered his men to bind him tightly to the mast so that he could hear the Sirens, and yet survive. As they rowed near the island Odysseus was so spellbound by the singing that he begged his men to release him. Unable to hear his pleas, the men rowed on as fast as they could and avoided disaster.

Circe's warning

Circe warned Odysseus of the dangers they would find on their way home. After they had passed the Sirens, they would come to the man-eating monster Scylla and Charybdis, a whirlpool that sucked down ships. She urged him to steer a course near Scylla's cave or Charybdis would almost certainly swallow up his crew.

What happened to the Sirens?

Some legends tell that the Sirens hurled themselves off the rocks to their death. They were so upset that Odysseus had not only heard their song, but also lived to warn others about it.

17

Scylla and Charybdis

Odysseus and his crew arrived at a narrow channel between steep cliffs. On one side lurked the treacherous Charybdis, on the other was the six-headed monster Scylla. Remembering Circe's advice, Odysseus told his terrified men to avoid Charybdis by sailing close to Scylla's cave. Then Odysseus armed himself and prepared to fight Scylla. But the creature was too quick for him. Her six long-necked heads darted in all directions, snatching six of Odysseus's men in her sharp teeth.

When the ship reached the other end of the channel, the men were dazed and exhausted. They decided to rest on the Sun God's island. Despite Odysseus's warning not to harm the grazing cattle, his men disobeyed. Zeus was furious and hurled a thunderbolt at the ship once they'd put to sea again. All the men were drowned, except Odysseus.

The Cattle of the Sun God

Odysseus had not wanted to land on the Sun God's island, but his men were exhausted and begged to rest. They promised not to harm the cattle, but when their food ran out they secretly killed and ate two of them. Remembering Tiresias's warning, Odysseus was horrified.

Ask the storyteller

Why did Zeus not punish Odysseus?
The Sun God asked Zeus, the king of the gods, to punish the men for killing his cattle. Odysseus was spared because he was the only one who had not eaten any of the meat.

Calypso and Nausicaa

Odysseus was washed up on the island of the nymph Calypso. All his crew had gone and he was very unhappy. Although he was glad to rest at Calypso's home for a few days, she wanted to keep Odysseus with her forever and wouldn't help him to leave. Feeling sorry for the hero, the gods sent their messenger, Hermes, to the island. After much persuasion, Calypso sadly agreed to let Odysseus go. She helped him make a raft and he soon set sail once again. Poseidon was furious when he saw this and smashed the raft to pieces. For days Odysseus was tossed in stormy seas before reaching the land of the Phaeacians. Here Princess Nausicaa found him and took him to her father's palace. When Odysseus told the Phaeacians his tragic story they gave him one of their ships, filled with gifts, and wished him a safe journey home.

Poseidon's rage

Poseidon was still angry with Odysseus for blinding his son, the cyclops Polyphemus. He was furious with the other gods for helping Odysseus and was determined to stop him from getting home.

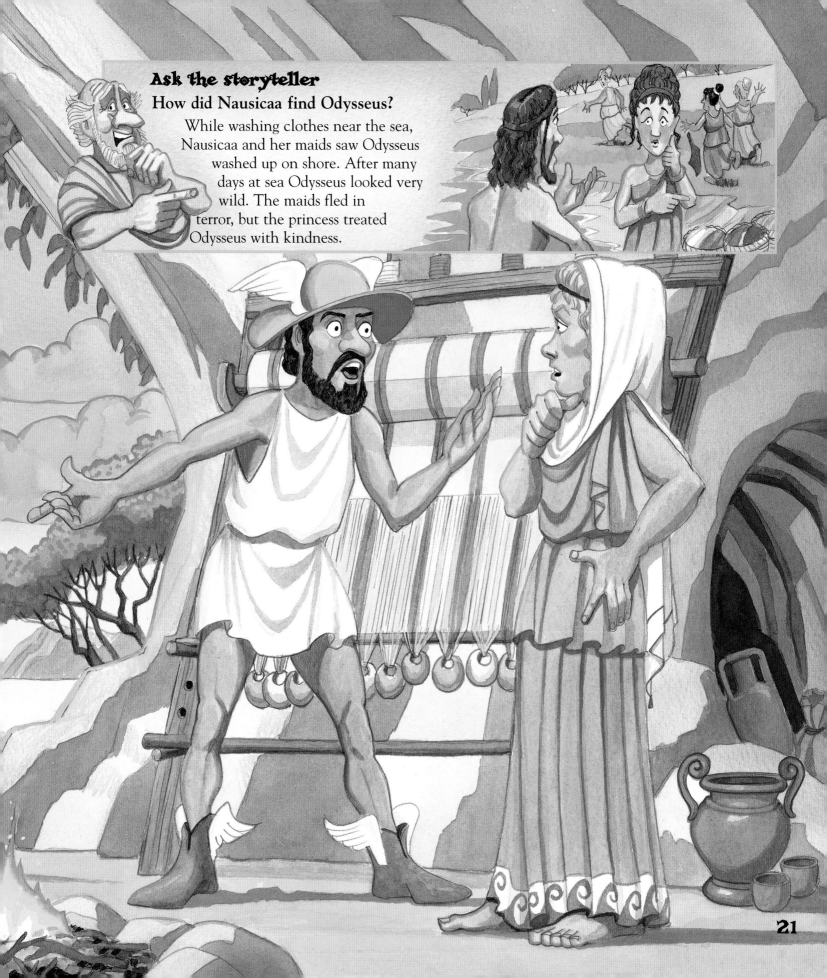

Ask the storyteller
How did Nausicaa find Odysseus?

While washing clothes near the sea, Nausicaa and her maids saw Odysseus washed up on shore. After many days at sea Odysseus looked very wild. The maids fled in terror, but the princess treated Odysseus with kindness.

Home at last!

Odysseus awoke on yet another beach, not knowing where he was. The Phaeacians' ship had gone and the land was shrouded in mist. Then it cleared, revealing the goddess Athena. When she told the hero that he was home in Ithaca Odysseus kissed the ground, overjoyed to be home at last. But Athena had brought the hero bad news too. She warned him that his life was in danger and told him to seek shelter at the home of his trusty swineherd, Eumaeus, until he'd worked out a plan to destroy his enemies. Athena disguised the hero as an aged beggar so that no one would recognise him. Grey-haired and leaning on a staff, Odysseus made his way to Eumaeus's hut. Eumaeus did not recognise his old master but greeted the beggar kindly, offering him food and shelter.

Odysseus at Eumaeus's hut

When Odysseus arrived at Eumaeus's hut his dogs bounded out and Eumaeus had to stop them from attacking the old beggar. Odysseus lied about who he was but told the doubting Eumaeus that Odysseus was alive and would soon be home.

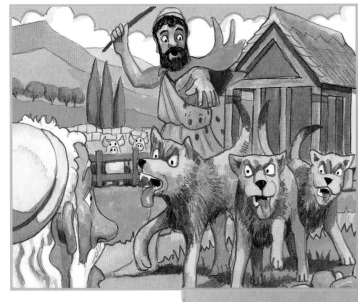

Why did Athena send Odysseus to stay with Eumaeus?

Athena wanted to help Odysseus and she knew that Eumaeus was one of the few people that Odysseus could trust.

The suitors of Penelope

In the twenty years that Odysseus had been away, things had not run smoothly on Ithaca. Most people believed that he would never return. For many years Odysseus's beautiful wife Penelope had been plagued by dozens of men eager to marry her and rule the kingdom in Odysseus's place. Penelope still loved Odysseus and didn't want to marry any of these men, but they refused to leave. They hung about the palace, gorging themselves on Odysseus's food and wine. They were also plotting to kill Odysseus's son and heir Telemachus. Telemachus knew that his life was in danger and when Athena instructed him to go to Eumaeus's hut he set off at once. There he was reunited with his long-lost father and together they worked out a plan to get rid of their troublesome enemies.

Penelope's plan

Penelope told the men that she could marry no one until she'd woven a shroud for Odysseus's father, Laertes, who was thought to be dead. Each night she secretly unpicked that day's work to delay her marriage. But a servant betrayed her and the men demanded that she marry one of them immediately.

Ask the storyteller

How was Odysseus reunited with his son?

Telemachus found it hard to believe that the beggar really was his father – even when Athena removed his disguise. Odysseus had left to fight the Trojans when his son was only an infant, who hardly knew him.

Jealous rivals

The next morning Odysseus travelled to the palace. He was still disguised as a beggar and only his old dog recognised him. The men jeered when they saw the elderly man and one of them threw a footstool at him. Odysseus was angry but knew that it was not yet the time for revenge. Irus, the brawny palace beggar, was not pleased to see someone else begging there. He challenged Odysseus to a boxing match. Odysseus agreed and astounded everyone by sending Irus sprawling with a single, well-timed blow. That night, when the men had gone home, Odysseus and Telemachus hid all the weapons they had left behind. Odysseus knew that they would be outnumbered in the fight and he would need all his strength and cunning to win. He was still trying to keep his true identity secret, but was recognised by his old nurse Eurycleia.

Ask the storyteller

How did Eurycleia recognise Odysseus?

While washing Odysseus's feet, Eurycleia saw a scar on his leg. It looked just like the one that Odysseus got from boar-hunting as a boy. Odysseus told Eurycleia to keep his secret until he could get rid of his enemies.

Just an old beggar

Penelope did not realise that the old beggar was her husband, Odysseus. She told him that she could no longer wait for her husband to return and must agree to marry another.

A good shot!

The next morning Penelope arranged an archery contest and said that she would marry the winner. The men were delighted, but none of them could even string the great bow which had belonged to Odysseus. They agreed to let the beggar try and to their horror, he won the contest easily. Then, disguised as a swallow, Athena led Odysseus, his son and Eumaeus on to kill all their enemies in a bloody fight. Odysseus revealed his true identity to Penelope and his father Laertes, whom he found working in the fields nearby. The families of the dead were furious with Odysseus and marched to the palace, wanting revenge. Finding the place in an uproar, the goddess Athena persuaded everyone to end their quarrel and live together peacefully again.

Odysseus and his bow

Penelope asked the men to use Odysseus's bow for the contest to test their prowess. To their amazement, the disguised Odysseus bent the great bow easily and won the contest by sending an arrow which pierced twelve axe heads that were lined up in a row.

Ask the storyteller

Was Penelope pleased to see Odysseus?

Even when Athena had removed Odysseus's
disguise Penelope did not recognise him.
It was only when Odysseus mentioned his bed,
which he had carved with his own hands,
that she believed it was him.

Glossary

Channel A narrow stretch of water between two land masses.

Cyclops Cave-dwelling giants who had only one eye.

Heir A person who will gain the possessions and titles of someone when they die.

Lotus A plant whose fruit made people dreamy and forgetful.

Moly A magical herb with a black root and white flower.

Nymph A beautiful young woman related to the gods.

Prophet A person who is able to tell what will happen in the future.

Prowess Skill or strength.

Sacrifice A person or animal that is killed and offered to the gods.

Shroud A sheet in which a dead body is wrapped.

Sirens Creatures who were part woman, part bird, who wrecked ships by enchanting sailors onto cliffs with their songs.

Sorceress A female magician who uses magic to bewitch people.

Suitor A man who is seeking a woman's hand in marriage.

Swineherd A person who looks after pigs.

Trojan War A war between the Greeks and the city of Troy, because a Trojan Prince stole the wife of a Greek king.

Underworld The place in Greek mythology where people go after they die.

Who's who

Achilles (a-KILL-eez) A Greek warrior who fought in the Trojan War.

Aeolus (eye-OH-luss) The god who controlled the winds.

Antiphates (an-TIFF-at-eez) King of the Laestrygonians.

Athena (a-THEE-na) Daughter of Zeus and the Greek goddess of wisdom and war.

Calypso (ka-LIP-so) An island nymph.

Charybdis (ka-RIB-diss) A monster that lived in a whirlpool and sucked down passing ships.

Cicones (kick-OH-neez) A tribe who lived near Ismarus.

Circe (KERR-key) A wicked sorceress who turned men into animals.

Eumaeus (you-MAY-us) The swineherd who sheltered Odysseus on his return to Ithaca.

Eurycleia (ure-ree-CLAY-a) Odysseus's nurse when he was a boy.

Hermes (HER-meez) The messenger of the gods, who wore winged sandals to carry him over land and sea.

Laestrygonians (lice-tree-GO-nee-ans) A race of man-eating giants.

Nausicaa (now-sick-AY-a) Phaeacian princess whose father helped Odysseus to get home.

Odysseus (Odd-ISS-ee-us) A Greek hero.

Penelope (pe-NELL-op-ee) The wife of Odysseus.

Phaeacians (fay-a-SEE-ans) A race of people who helped Odysseus get home.

Polyphemus (poll-ee-FEE-muss) A cyclops.

Poseidon (poss-EYE-don) The Greek god of the sea.

Scylla (SILL-a) A six-headed, man-eating monster that lived in a cave.

Sisyphus (SISS-if-us) A man who had to spend his time in the Underworld trying to roll a boulder up a mountain.

Tiresias (tie-REE-see-ass) The dead prophet of the Underworld.

Telemachus (tell-EM-a-kuss) Son and heir of Odysseus.

Zeus (ZYOOS) King of the Greek gods.

Index